THIS MONSTER'S GOT NO TEETH! WHAT'S HE GOING TO DO, GUM US TO DEATH?

ZINI, COME ON. LOOK AT THAT SWEET LITTLE FACE. DOES THAT LOOK LIKE A MONSTER TO YOU?

SO THE LEMURS RAISE THE IGUANADON AS THEIR OWN.

MANY YEARS LATER, A GROUP OF YOUNG LEMURS SCRAMBLE FOR COVER!

ROARRRR!

RAAARRRR!

ROOOARR!

YOUNG SURI, PLIO'S DAUGHTER, ESCAPES UP A TREE...

BUT TOO LATE?

GASP!

LET ME OUT! LET ME OUT!

CHOMP!

THE LIGHT TURNS TO DARKNESS. AN EERIE WIND WHIPS THROUGH THE TREES.

WHOOOOOOSSSH!

THE LEMURS ARE KNOCKED BACK BY A SHOCKWAVE!

WHOOOOOOOSSSH!

SURI!! WHERE ARE YOU!?

MUM!

RRRRUMBLE RRRRUMBLE RRRRUMBLE

ALADAR RESCUES SURI FROM A TREE JUST IN TIME.

CRRRAASH!

THE FOREST BURNS! CRATERS EXPLODE!

CRRRAASH!

BOOOM!

RRRRUMBLE

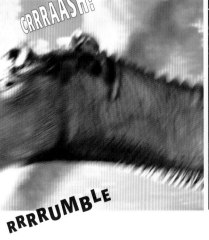

ZINI, JUMP! JUMP!!

CRRRAASH!

ZINI NARROWLY ESCAPES BEING CRUSHED!

A GIGANTIC WAVE OF FIRE ROLLS TOWARDS LEMUR ISLAND!

FFOOOOOM!

RRRRUMBLE

BLAM!

RRRRUMBLE

ALADAR RACES AWAY, LEMURS CLINGING TO HIS BACK!

HE REACHES THE STEEP CLIFFS AT THE EDGE OF THEIR SMALL ISLAND.

THE SEA BELOW IS THE ONLY ESCAPE FROM A FIERY DEATH...

BOOOM!

KER-SPLASH!

PLIO! YAR! WHERE ARE YOU?

OVER HERE!

AS THE RAPTORS NIP AT ALADAR, THE LEMURS STRUGGLE TO KEEP THEIR BALANCE!

THE RAPTORS CLOSE IN!

SNAP!

HISSSSS!

REACHING FLAT GROUND, ALADAR RUNS AS FAST AS HE CAN!

YAR! GRAB ON!

YAR LOSES HIS BALANCE!

SNAP!

PLIO AND ZINI PULL HIM TO SAFETY!

JUST AS THE RAPTORS BEGIN A FINAL, LETHAL ATTACK.

BUT TO THE AMAZEMENT OF ALADAR AND THE LEMURS, THE RAPTORS SLOW DOWN!

ALADAR, THEY'RE STOPPING!

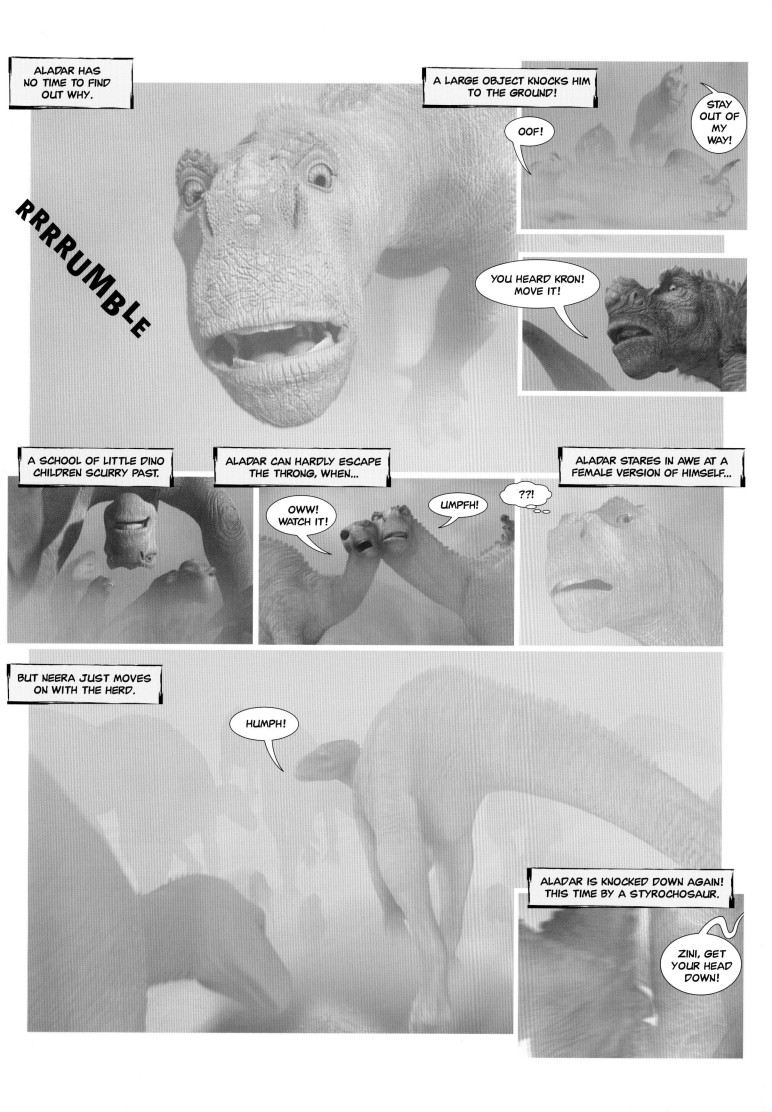

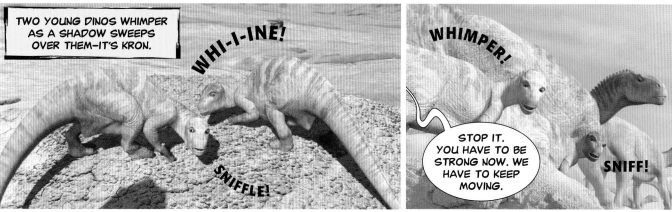